The k

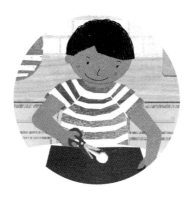

Kasia Reay

Illustrated by Ruth Waters

Schofield&Sims

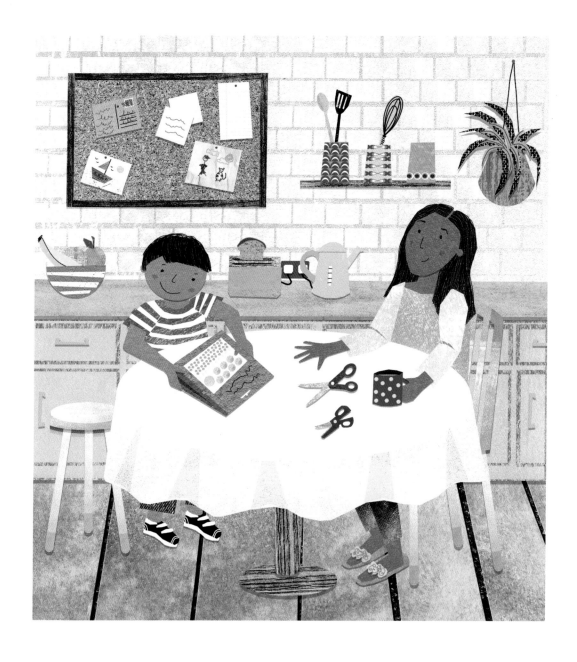

San got a kit to cut.

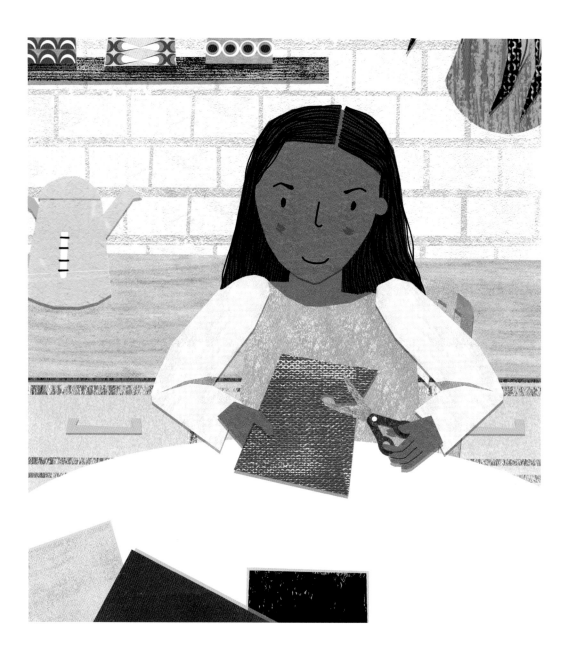

Mum got a dot to cut.

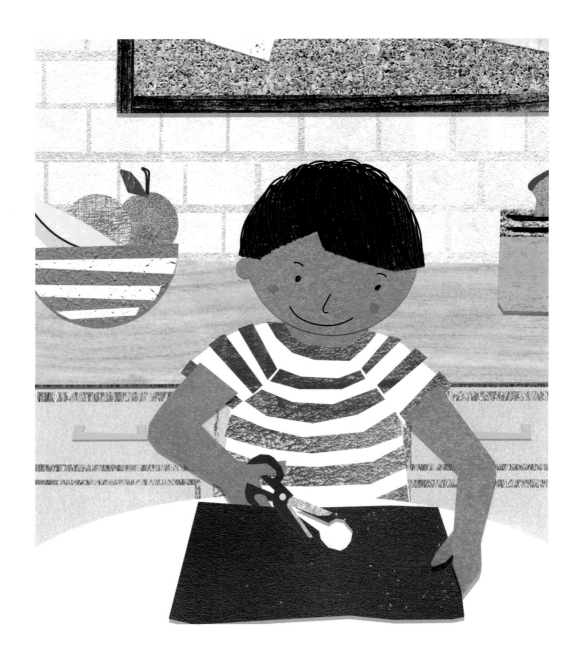

San got a dot to cut.

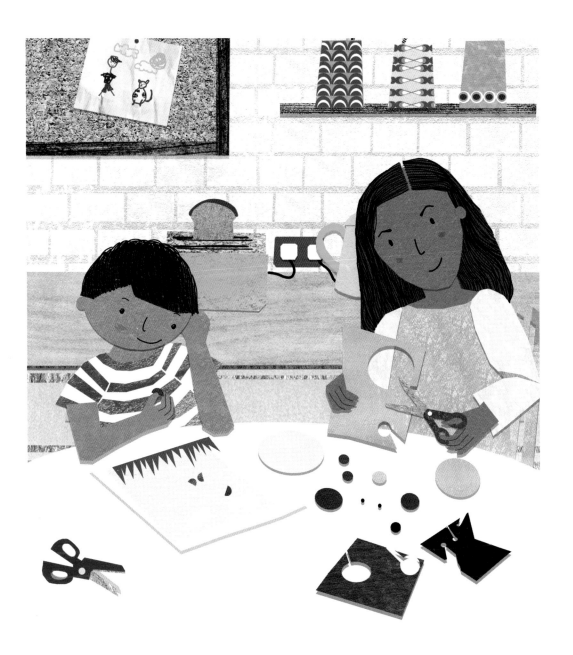

Mum got ten to cut.

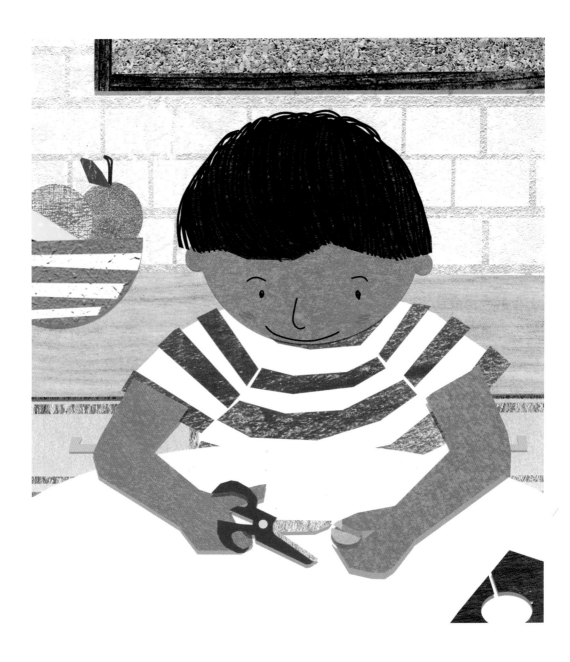

San got a dot to cut.

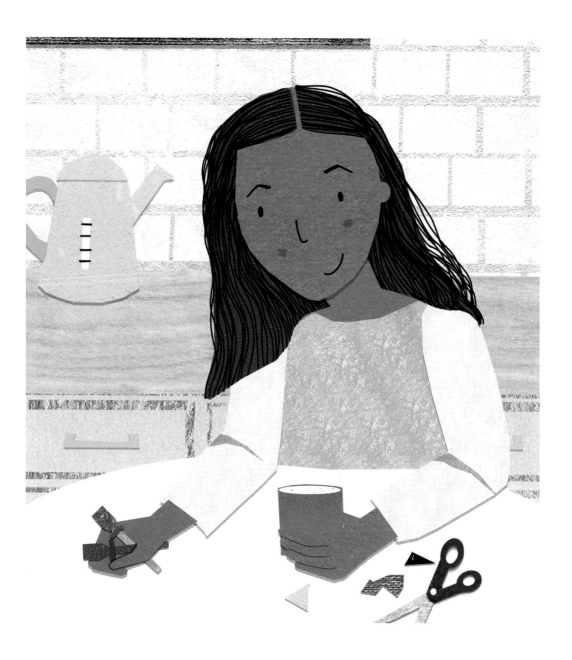

Mum got a pot.

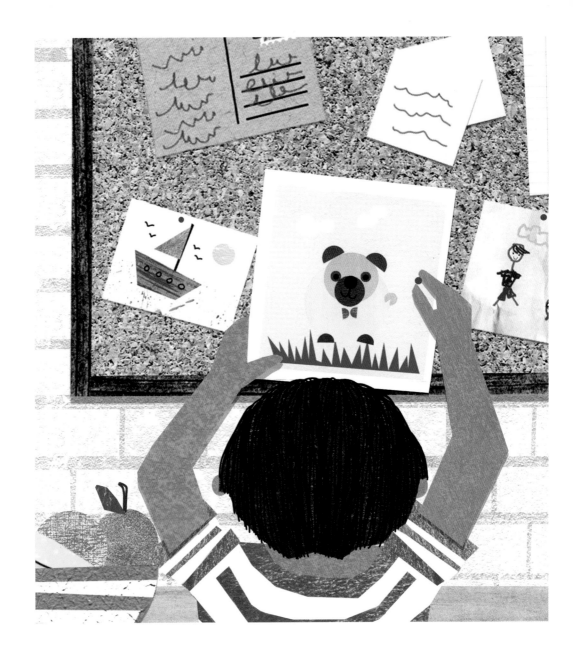

San got a pug to pin up!